The Good Neighbors
Store an Award

A Cheesy Mouse Tale of Addition with Regrouping

GOOD
NEIGHBOR
AWARD

ONESIE
TENOR
HUND-RED

Written by Mark Ramsay • Illustrated by Susan G. Robinson

STRATEGIC
Educational Tools

For my wife Melissa,
who supported my dream.
- MR

For my grandfather,
who always provided me
with markers, paper and
plenty of good cheese.
- SR

Published by
Strategic Educational Tools
293 Center Street
East Aurora, New York 14052
www.strategicedtools.com

Text © 2009 by Mark Ramsay
Illustrations © 2009 by Susan G. Robinson

Book design and cover by Susan G. Robinson.
Edited by Nancy Raines Day.

Printed in the United States of America.
First Edition

Publisher's Cataloging-in-Publication data

Ramsay, Mark, 1968-
The good neighbors store an award - a cheesy mouse tale of addition with
regrouping / written by Mark Ramsay ; illustrated by Susan G. Robinson.
p. cm.
Series : The good neighbors math series
Summary: When the Good Neighbors are each awarded pieces of cheese,
they must use what they know about addition with regrouping, the base-ten
number system, base-ten blocks, and place value to store it all safely inside
their houses.
ISBN 978-0-9842863-0-0 [1. Mathematics--Fiction. 2. Arithmetic--Fiction. 3.
Addition--Fiction.] I. Robinson, Susan Gail. II. Title.

PZ7.R145 Go 2010
[E]—dc22   2009910457

Hello, my neighbors call me Onesie.

I guess it's because I wear a one-piece outfit
with my favorite number on the front.

I live next-door to Tenor.
He *loves* to sing in his high-pitched voice.

Tenor lives next-door to Hund-Red,
the most glowing and generous mouse you will ever meet.

We all love cheese - no matter what its size!

I eat small cheese cubes,
the same cubes that make up
the bigger pieces of cheese.

Tenor eats medium-sized cheese sticks...

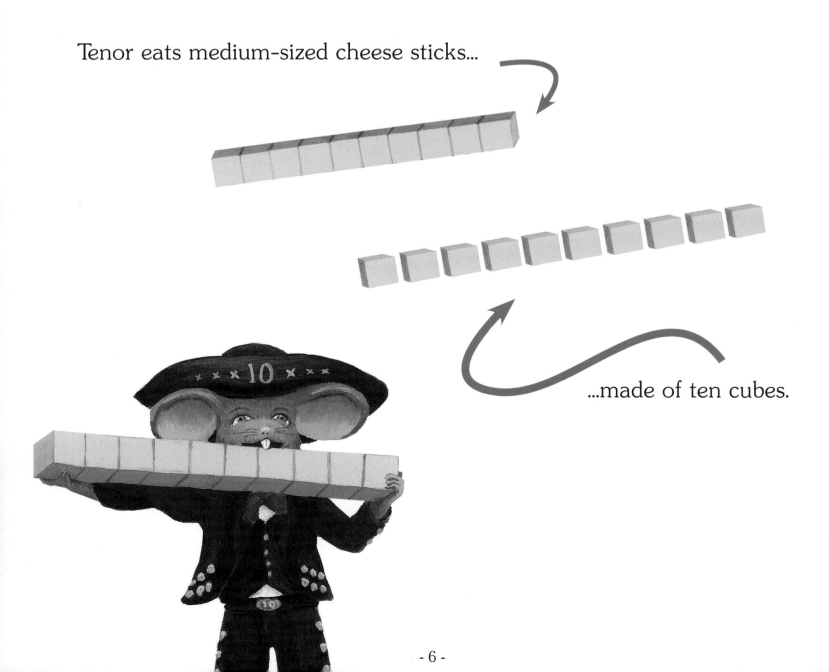

...made of ten cubes.

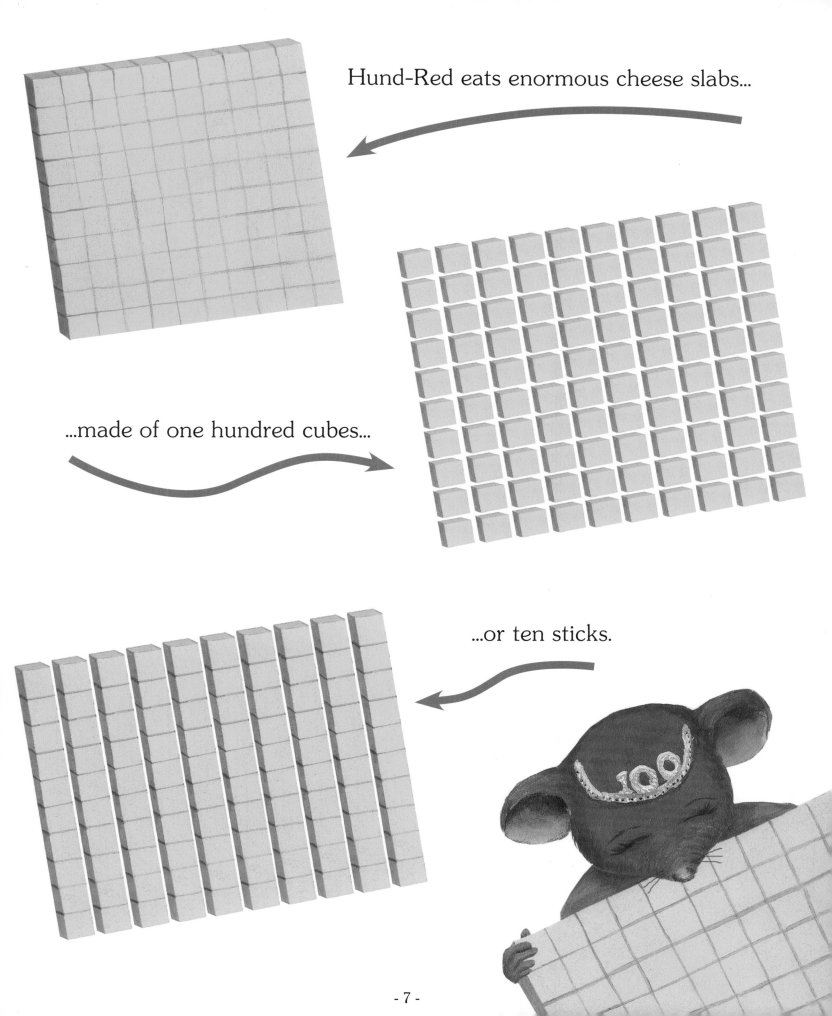

Hund-Red eats enormous cheese slabs...

...made of one hundred cubes...

...or ten sticks.

- 7 -

Every Monday morning, we rush to the cheese factory
to stock up on cheese.

We can each store up to nine pieces of our favorite size of cheese,
so we buy the amount we need to fill up our homes.

When all three of our houses are full of cheese,
how many **cubes** would that make altogether?
Look back at pages 4 and 5 if you need a hint.

Even though we each buy and store our own cheese...

...we believe that it belongs to all of us.

Our motto is,
Mi queso es su queso (mee KAY-so es soo KAY-so),
which means *My cheese is your cheese* in Spanish.

Now that you know all about my two neighbors and me,
let me tell you about our award.

On Saturday, after five days of cheese eating, the mayor and his three
assistants paid us a surprise visit.

The mayor declared, "Onesie, Tenor, and Hund-Red, I am pleased to present you with the Good Neighbor Award.

You work and play together so well, but more importantly, you help each other and share.

From now on, you three will be called The Good Neighbors. In addition to this lovely plaque, I award you each five pieces of your favorite size of cheese."

How many **cubes** would our award make altogether?

"Let's go store our award!" we cheered.

How much cheese did each of us already have at home?
How many **cubes** would that make altogether?

Once home, I quickly saw a problem.

I had twelve cubes!

Do you know why having twelve cubes was a problem?

So I carted ten of my twelve cubes over to Tenor's house.

Phew! This is work! I hope he'll help me.

Do you know why I brought ten cubes?
How many cubes did I leave at home?

Tenor looked at my cheese,
       then looked at me.

"Uh-oh!" sang Tenor.
"Storage problem, *amigo*?"

Tenor lit his cheese torch.

♪ Stand back! 🎵

He melted one side of a cube...

...and stuck it to the next cube.

He kept on melting and sticking cubes together
until all ten cubes became one...

...CHEESE STICK!

TA-DA!

"Now I'll have *plenty*
of room back home for my
two cubes. *Gracias!*" I said.

"No *problema!* Come over
any time you need cheese.
Mi queso es su queso!" sang Tenor.

Tenor glanced at his cheese outside, then peeked at his cheese inside.

"Fourteen sticks!" he shrieked.
"I'm drowning in cheese! Hund-Red, HELP!"

Do you know why Tenor needed Hund-Red's help?

So Tenor hauled ten of his fourteen sticks over to Hund-Red's house.

Do you know why Tenor brought ten sticks?
How many sticks did he leave at home?

Hund-Red looked at Tenor's cheese, then looked at him.

"Good thing I have such a *casa grande*," she said.

Hund-Red lit her cheese torch.

She melted one side of a stick...

...and stuck it to the next stick.

She kept on melting and sticking sticks together
until all ten sticks became one...

...CHEESE SLAB!

TA-DA!

"*Gracias.* Now I'll have *loads* of room back home for my four cheese sticks, and you're going to have a house full of cheese – nine slabs!" piped Tenor.

"It's not about the cheese. It's about helping the needy! Come over any time you need cheese. *Mi queso es su queso!*" said Hund-Red.

We did it.
We stored our award!

How much cheese did each of us have?
*How many **cubes** would that make altogether?*

Later that day, we met outside to admire our new plaque...

Rockabye and goodnight!
Guess I'll have to *snack* later.
Grrrrr
ZZZZZZZZZZZZZ

The Good Neighbors Store an Award
CHEESY SUMMARY

Hund-Red
(Slabs)

Cheese from neighbor

plus +

Cheese before Good Neighbor Award

plus +

Good Neighbor Award cheese to be stored

equals =

Cheese after storing Good Neighbor Award

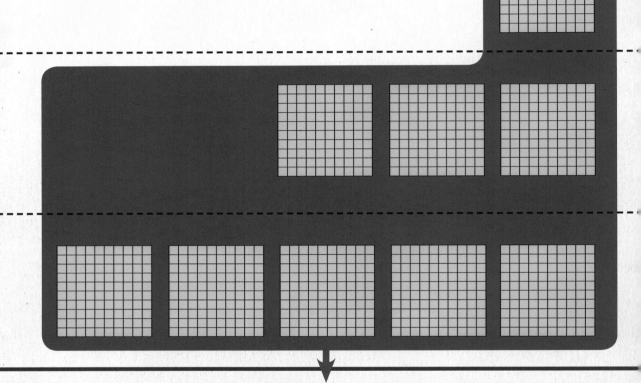

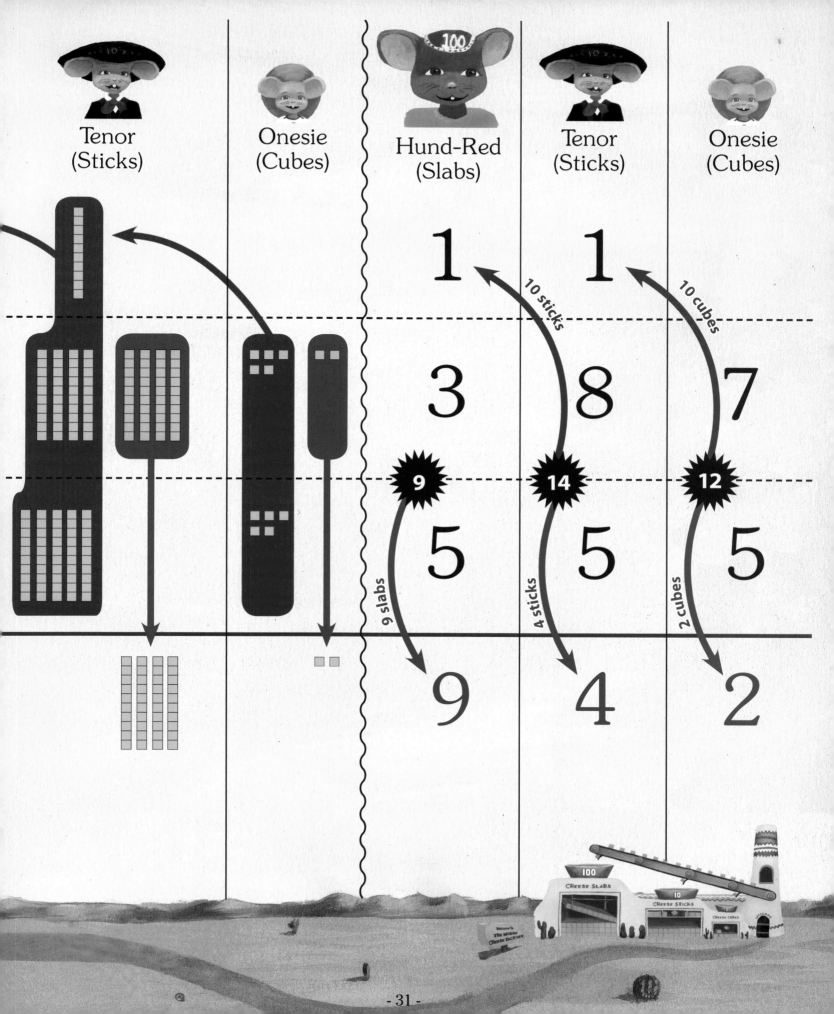

The Good Neighbors Math Series

The Good Neighbors Store an Award -
A Cheesy Mouse Tale of Addition with Regrouping

When The Good Neighbors each receive a cheesy award, some of the mice discover that they do not have enough room to store it all safely inside their houses. Can The Good Neighbors work together to solve their cheese storage problem? The mice's story models the addition with regrouping process as demonstrated with base-ten blocks.

The Good Neighbors' Cheese Feast -
A Cheesy Mouse Tale of Subtraction with Regrouping

When The Good Neighbors decide to have a cheese feast, some of the mice discover that they do not have enough cheese to make their cheesy dishes. Can The Good Neighbors work together to solve their cheese shortage problem? The mice's story models the subtraction with regrouping process as demonstrated with base-ten blocks.

Look for new books and accessories coming soon!

Visit *The Good Neighbors Math Series* at www.strategicedtools.com!

- Purchase books and accessories
- Download free activity sheets
- Receive instructional ideas and tips